Dig It Up

Jan Joss

ILLUSTRATED BY
Sherry Neidigh

© 1998 Journey Books
Published by Bob Jones University Press
Greenville, SC 29614
ISBN 0-89084-981-1

A tub is in the sand.

Diggedy,
    diggedy,
        dig it up.

Here it is!

3

Chen handed
the butter tub
to Mother.

A mug is in the sand.

5

Diggedy,
   diggedy,
      dig it up.

Here it is!

Chen handed
the yellow mug
to Mother.

A can is in the sand.

Diggedy,
diggedy,
dig it up.

Here it is!

Chen handed
the dented can
to Mother.

10

A duck is in the sand.

Diggedy,
  diggedy,
    dig it up.

Here it is!

Chen handed
the rubber duck
to Mother.

13

A rubber duck,
a dented can,
a yellow mug,
and
a butter tub . . .

are back in the sand!

Can a pig dig?

back   tub   dig
tack   sub   pig
sack   cub   wig

Service words:

  a mother

Enrichment words:

  butter diggedy rubber yellow

Structural words:

  handed dented